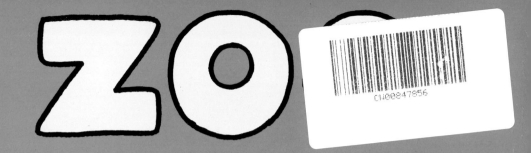

ZOO

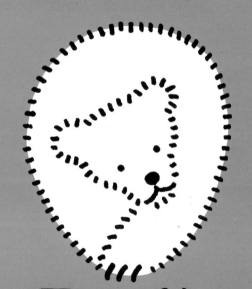

Jan Pieńkowski
PUFFIN BOOKS

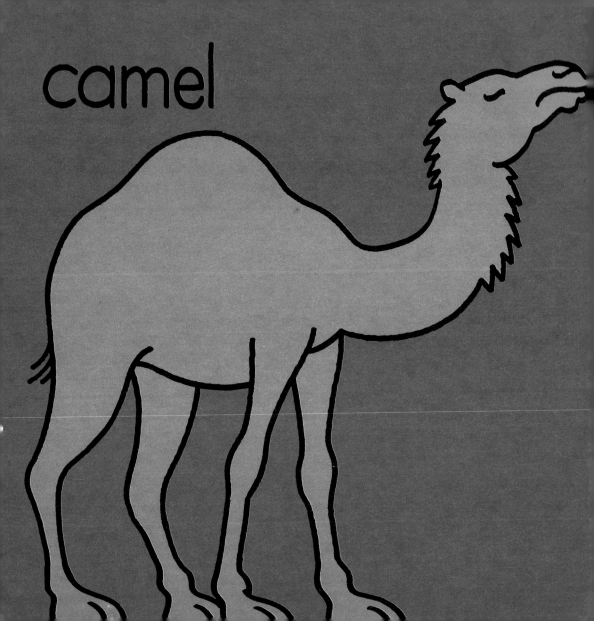

camel

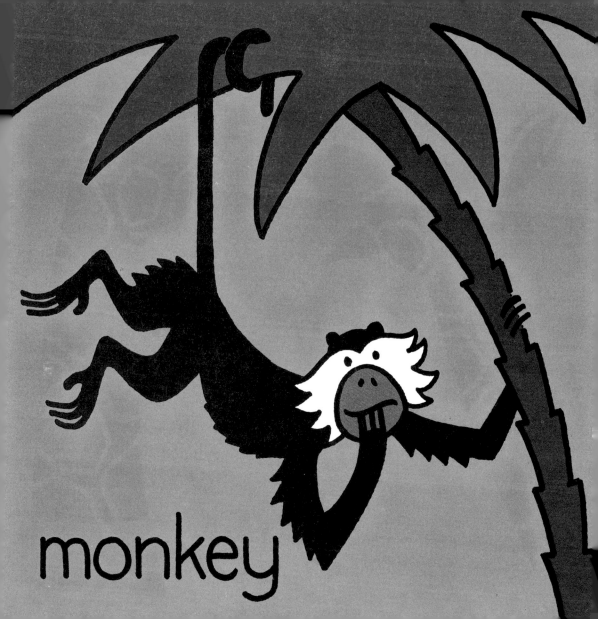

monkey

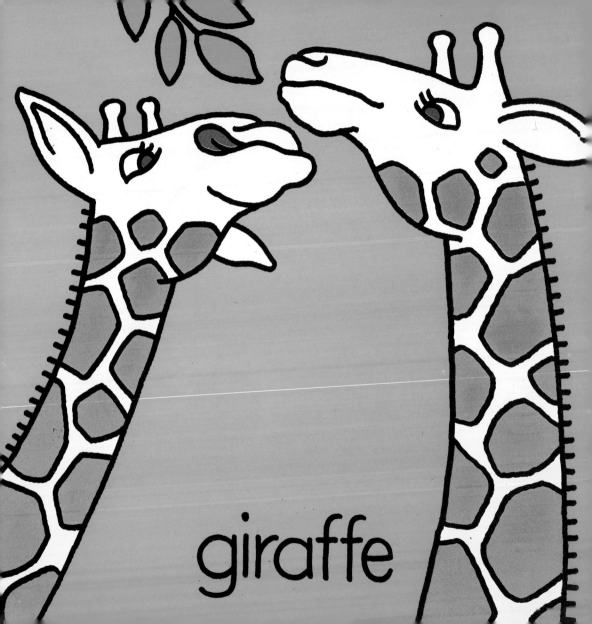

giraffe

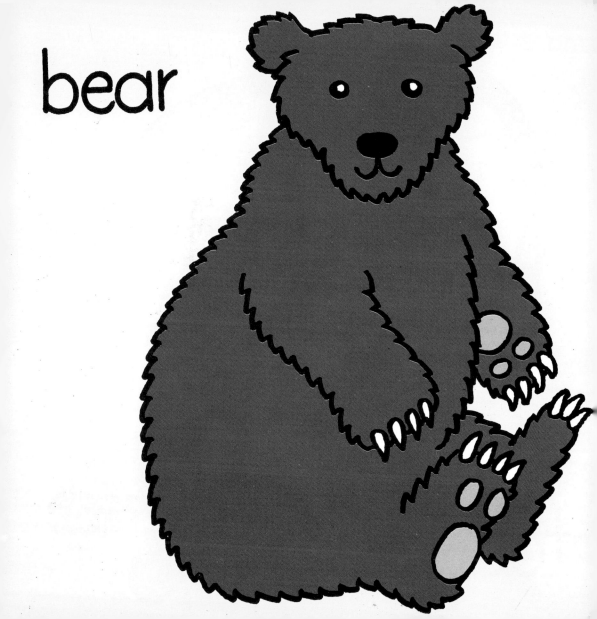

bear

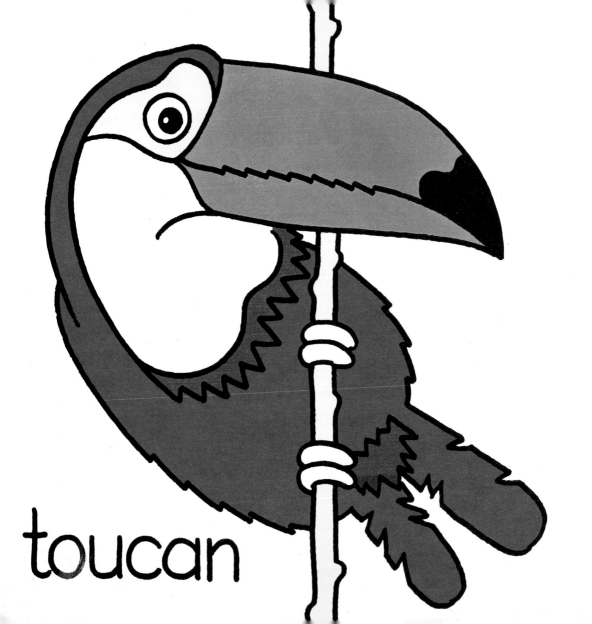

toucan

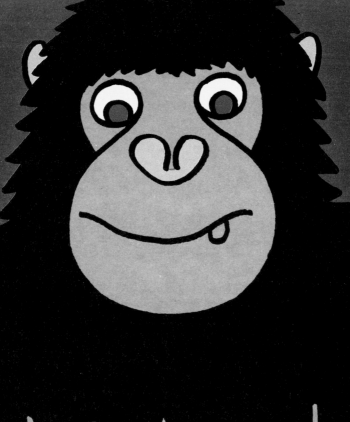

gorilla

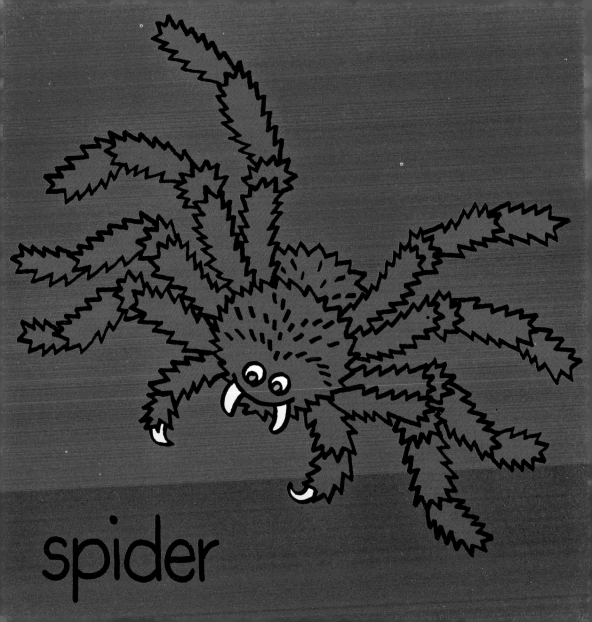

spider

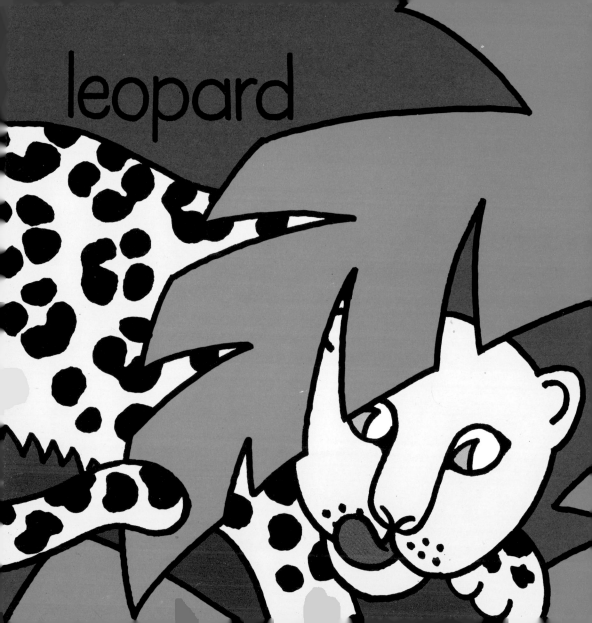

leopard

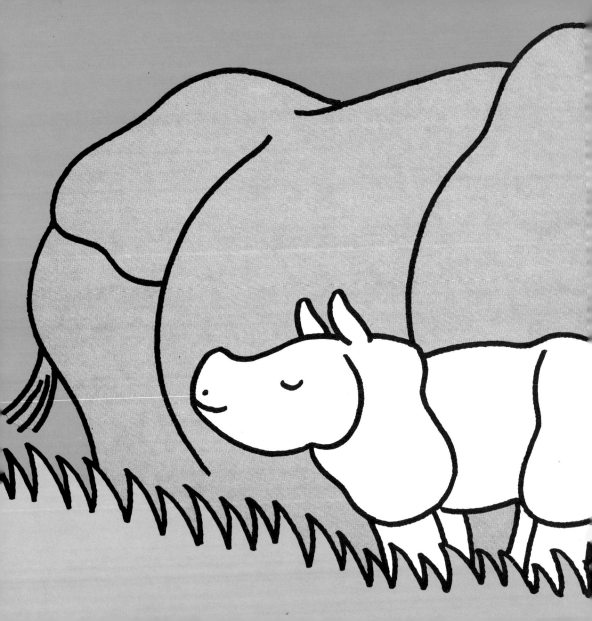

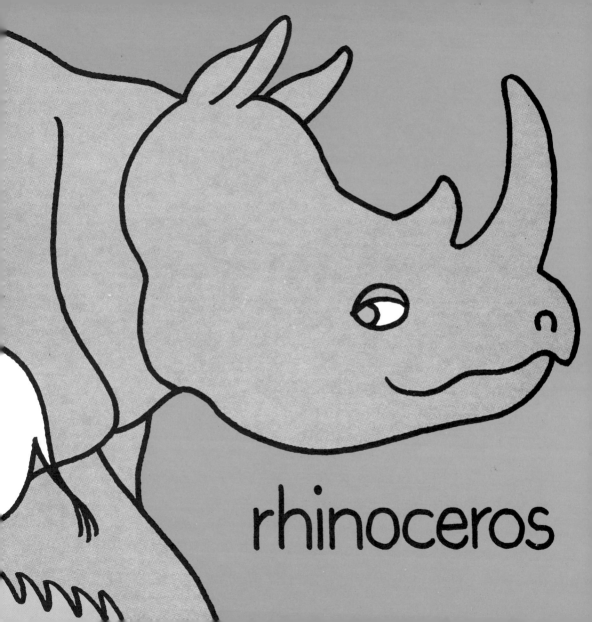

rhinoceros

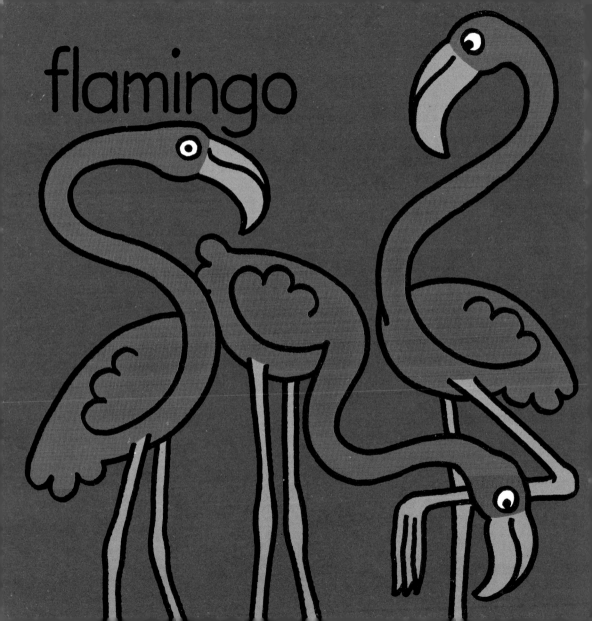

flamingo

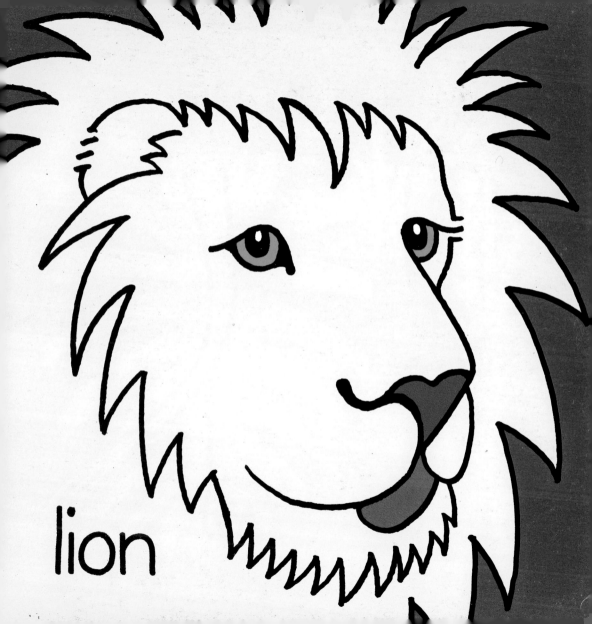

lion

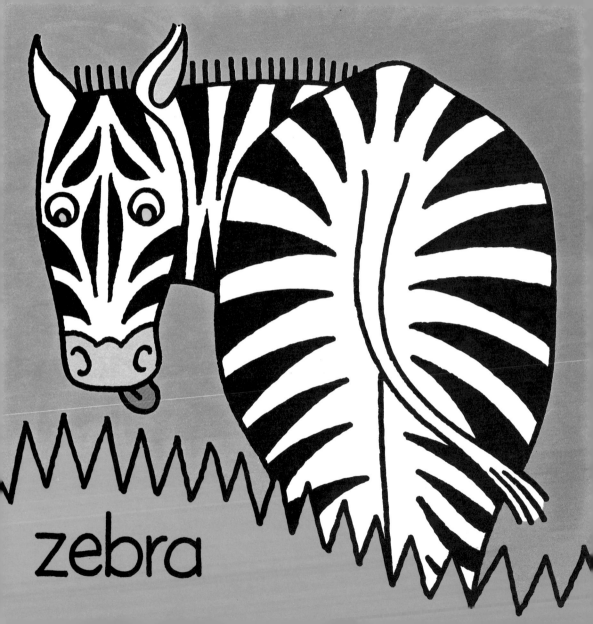

zebra

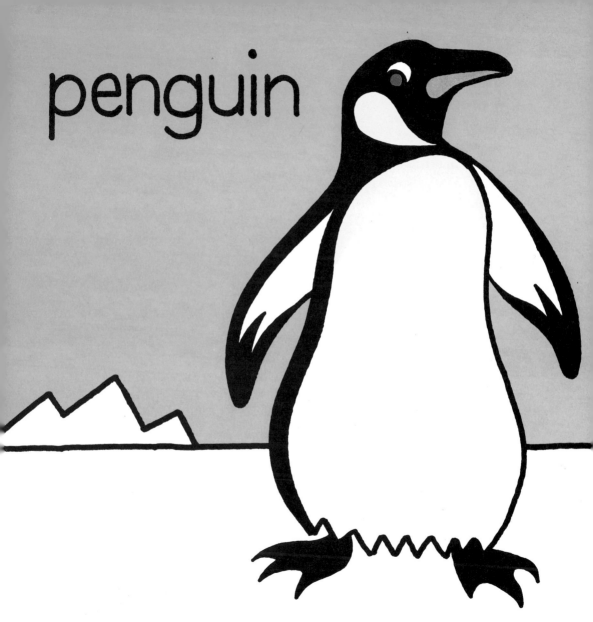

penguin

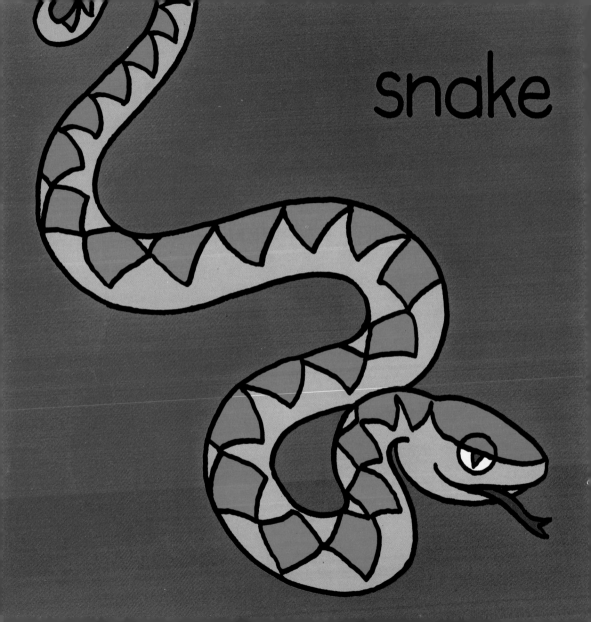

snake

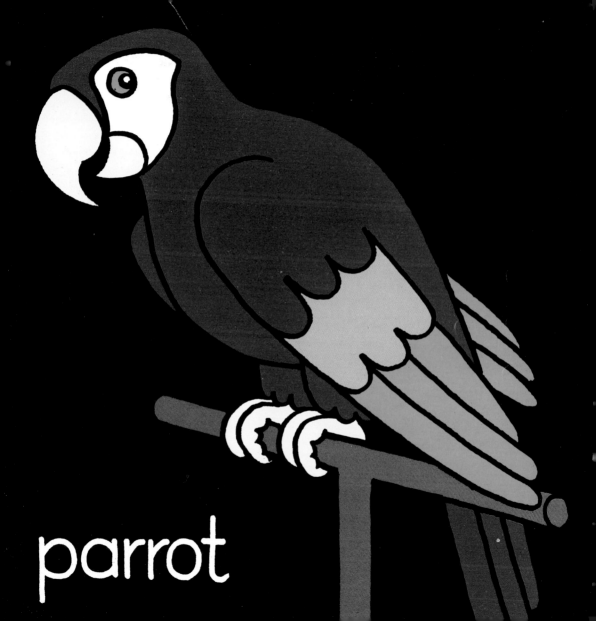

parrot

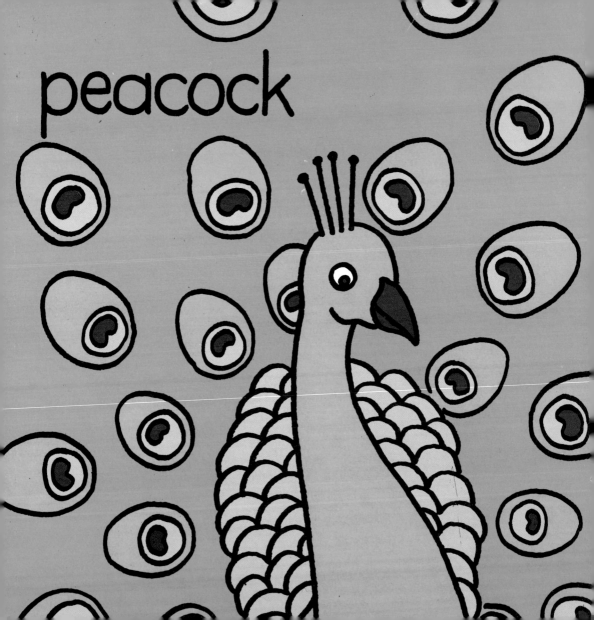

peacock

koala

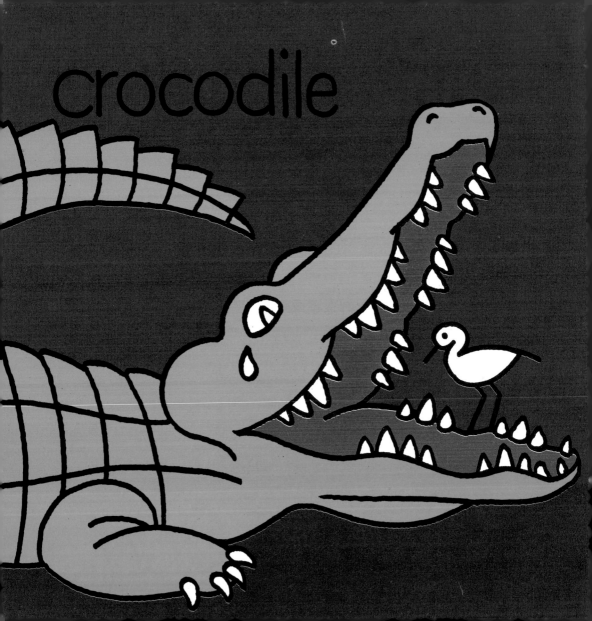

crocodile

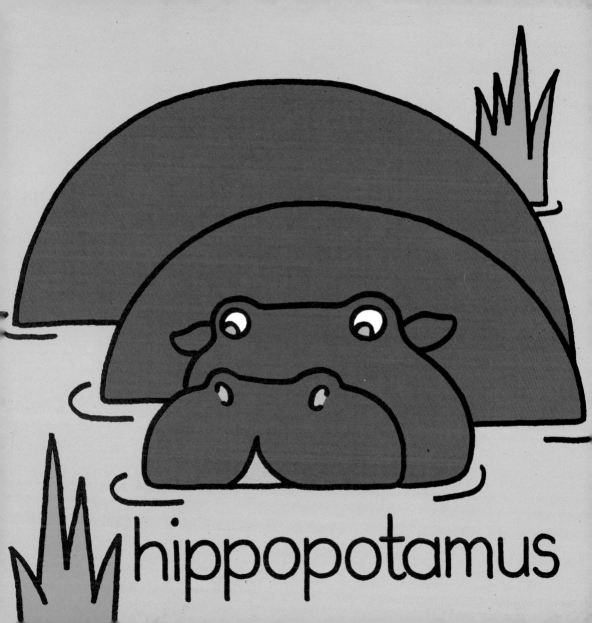

hippopotamus

what animal?

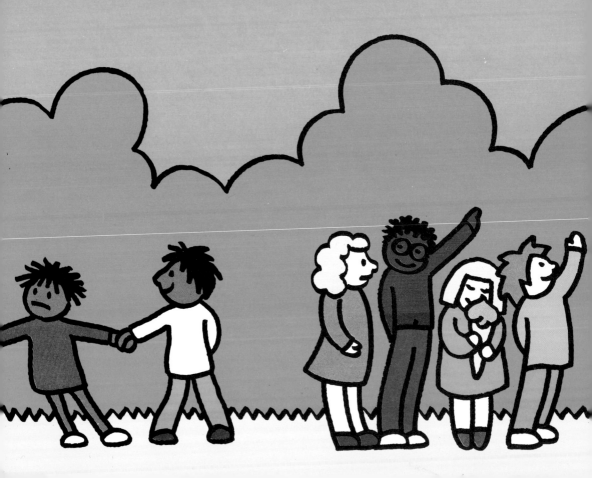

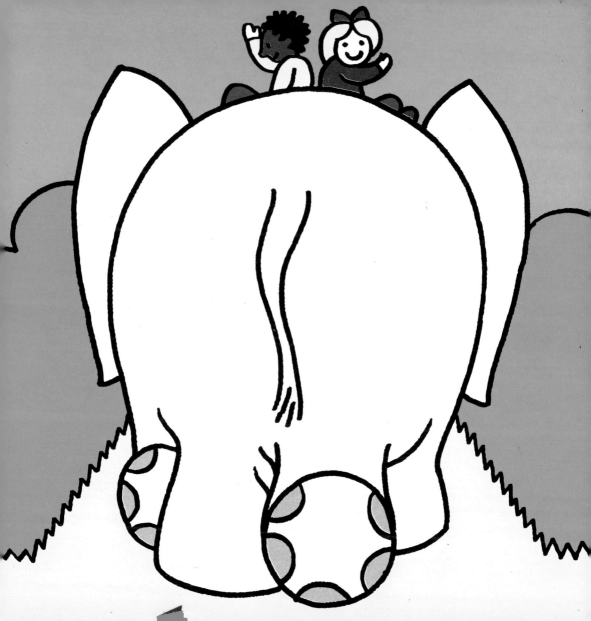

goodbye!

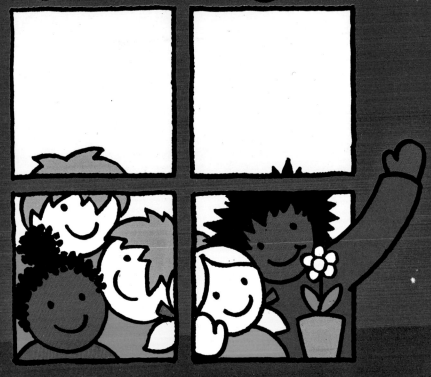